Tell me . . .

. . . about the Holy Spirit
and the Church

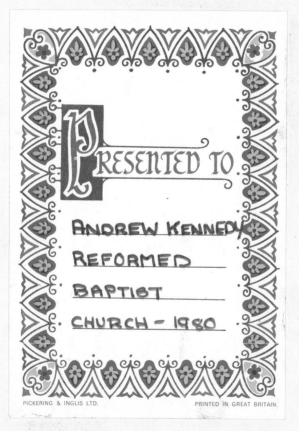

PRESENTED TO

ANDREW KENNEDY

REFORMED

BAPTIST

CHURCH – 1980

PICKERING & INGLIS LTD.   PRINTED IN GREAT BRITAIN

3

Tell me ...
... about the Holy Spirit and the Church

DEREK PRIME

VICTORY PRESS
EASTBOURNE

This series based on 'Tell me the answer'
books which were first published in 1965.
This new series © Derek Prime 1975

ISBN 0 85476 235 3

Illustrations and cover design
by Elsie Sands

Printed in Great Britain for
Victory Press (Evangelical Publishers Ltd.),
Lottbridge Drove, Eastbourne, E. Sussex,
by Richard Clay (The Chaucer Press) Ltd.,
Bungay, Suffolk.

1

Breaking up

Joanna Price woke up before her twin brother, Stephen. She listened, but couldn't hear a sound. So it couldn't have been her parents' alarm clock which had woken her up. She crept downstairs to the hall to see what the time was. Only a quarter past six! Another three quarters of an hour before the alarm would go.

What a lovely day! Joanna was so excited. It was Friday, the Friday before Whitsun and the Spring holiday, and after school that day, there would be a week's half-term holiday. Mr. Price was going to take part of his holiday during that week, and he had promised to take them down to Grannie and Grandad's bungalow at the seaside. Grannie and Grandad had offered to stay in Stephen and Joanna's home in exchange, to look after the cat and the goldfish.

Joanna was bursting with ideas of things to do. She decided to wake up Stephen, and tip-toed into his bedroom.

"Wake up, Steve!" she said, not too loudly, in the ear which was uppermost.

"Err, what is it?" yawned Stephen. "It can't be time to get up yet!"

"No, not yet. Another three quarters of an hour."

"Well what did you want to wake me up for then, silly?" said Stephen. "I'm tired. Go back to bed and leave me alone."

And he turned over on the other side and pulled the blankets over his head.

"Oh no you don't, you old lazybones," exclaimed Joanna. "We break up today, remember? And it's time we made our plans for half-term."

The thought of breaking up made Stephen feel much happier. "So it is. Right, what are we going to do?" he shouted.

"SSh!" whispered Joanna. "Mummy and Daddy are still asleep. Don't make such a noise. Look, I've found Daddy's guide-book, and from the look of it, there are all kinds of interesting things to explore near where we'll be staying. There's a castle about ten miles away, and the ruins of an old monastery not far off. And there's an old Norman church, like the one we saw in our magazine a few weeks ago. That's quite near too."

"Only hope the weather's decent," commented Stephen.

"Daddy said the weather was good this time last year," replied Joanna. "Let's write down what we want to do when we get there."

*   *   *

"You look happy, Steve," commented Mr. Price, as Stephen came leaping down for breakfast.

"I am," answered Stephen. "We're breaking up, and Jo and I have been making a list of all the things we're going to do."

"We're going to put up the tent in the garden tomorrow if the weather's O.K.," added Joanna, who had just come down.

"It's good having another holiday so soon after Easter, isn't it?" said Stephen.

Mr. Price smiled and nodded. He was looking forward to the holiday too. But he wondered whether the twins had remembered that this year the Spring holiday week-end was also Whitsun.

"Have you had a lesson at school about Whitsun?" he asked.

"Yes," replied Joanna, "Mrs. Foxleigh knows I go to Sunday School and she made me tell everyone else all about Whitsun."

"What did you say?" asked her father.

"I told them that it's the time when we remember that God sent the Holy Spirit to the disciples as they waited at Jerusalem. I had to say what happened to the disciples: how they were made very bold, and could tell everyone about the Lord Jesus."

"Lay the table for breakfast, please!" called Mrs. Price from the kitchen. "What do you want this morning? Scrambled eggs or egg and bacon?"

"Egg and bacon, please," shouted Stephen and Joanna in chorus.

Joanna fetched the cloth, and Stephen counted out the right number of knives and forks.

"Did it come into the world for the first time at Whitsun?" he asked suddenly.

"I don't know what you mean," said Mr. Price, who was still thinking of eggs and bacon.

"I mean the Holy Spirit," exclaimed Stephen.

"You're making a mistake, then," replied his father.

"How?"

"Do you know, Jo?"

She thought for a moment. "Yes, I think so. Steve said 'Did *it* come into the world for the first time?' didn't he? But the Holy Spirit's not *it*; He's *He*!"

Mr. Price nodded. "That's right. You speak of a thing as *it*. If we were talking about the car, we might say, '*It* needs a clean'. Or we might say about the phone, '*It*'s ringing'. But if we saw the milkman coming up the path, we'd say, 'Here *he* comes' because the milkman's a person. The Holy Spirit isn't a thing, He's a Person. When the Lord Jesus spoke about the Holy Spirit, He always called Him 'He' and never 'it'. How would you like to be called 'it', Steve, instead of 'him'?"

"I wouldn't," retorted Stephen.

"You've learned something, then. Remember, the Holy Spirit's a Person; we may upset Him and grieve Him by our sin, even as you and I may upset each other by doing wrong things."

"Well then," said Stephen patiently, "did *He* come into the world for the first time that Whitsun?"

"What do you think?" Mr. Price was sure that Stephen and Joanna ought to be able to answer this themselves.

Stephen and Joanna looked at one another. After a while, Mr. Price thought he'd better help them. "Well, can you remember us talking about the Holy Spirit before?"

Joanna could. "Yes, when you explained to us about the Trinity—how there's only one God, but He makes Himself known to us in three persons."

"Good," said Mr. Price. "Now, can you remember the passage in the Bible—I think Mummy told you about it—where it tells us about God the

Father, the Son and the Holy Spirit doing something together?"

"Yes, I know," Stephen remembered. "It was Jesus' baptism. God the Father spoke from heaven. And then the Holy Spirit came down on Jesus, like a dove."

Mr. Price smiled, "Yes, that's right. Now you've almost answered your own question."

"Oh, I see," said Stephen. "The Holy Spirit was here on earth before the first Whitsun, because He was with the Lord Jesus when He was on earth."

"There's more to it than that," Mr. Price went on. "The Holy Spirit had a lot to do with the coming of the Lord Jesus to live in this world. He made possible the birth of the Lord Jesus without a human father. He helped the Lord Jesus in the wonderful things He did, and the Holy Spirit raised the Lord Jesus from the dead, too."

"I didn't know He did all those things!" exclaimed Joanna in surprise. "But did the Holy Spirit ever help people like us?"

"Yes, He did. For example, He helped all the people who wrote the Bible. He made them feel they ought to write down some of God's message to them. Even when they didn't completely understand what it all meant, He showed them what to write. He helped them to write about things in the future which no one else knew would happen. He let them into some of God's secrets, to prepare people for them."

"I ought to have remembered that," Stephen said.

By now the smell of eggs and bacon was wafting into the room. "Mmmm! Smells good," murmured Mr. Price.

"Did the Holy Spirit do anything else before Jesus came, Daddy?" asked Joanna.

"He certainly did," answered Mr. Price. "He helped with the creation of the world. The first chapter of the Bible tells us something about that. All the beautiful things you see in the world—the birds, the animals, the trees, the flowers—are His work. Whenever you see something wonderful and beautiful in the world, you may be sure that it is the work of God the Holy Spirit."

"So it was a bit silly to ask if He began His work at Whitsun, wasn't it?" Stephen looked sheepish.

"No, it wasn't silly at all," replied Mr. Price. "It's good to ask questions; that's how we learn, after all. The Holy Spirit didn't come into the world for the first time at Whitsun; but He did come in a new and special way at Whitsun, to be with Christians and to live in them. I'm sure we'll hear something about Him at church on Sunday. Let's go and see how much we can learn; then perhaps we can talk about it all on our way home."

At that moment Mrs. Price appeared with two plates of bacon and egg. "Bring the other two in, please, Jo," she said in a fluster. "And I suggest you stop talking for two minutes and eat your breakfast! You'll be late for school at this rate."

Mr. Price glanced at his watch and gave a horrified gasp. "And I'll be late for my train, which is more to the point!"

2

Whit Sunday

Whit Sunday was hot, and by the time the Prices were halfway through their dinner, Stephen could think of nothing else but the seaside.

"Phew!" he exclaimed, while his mother was dividing up the apple crumble. "I wish we were at Grannie and Grandad's now."

"Patience!" Mr. Price smiled. "Yes, and wasn't it warm in church this morning? I'm glad they opened all the windows."

"There were lots of people away on holiday, weren't there?' commented his wife, as she passed the plates round. "Help yourselves to the custard, everybody."

"Quite a few visitors to make up for it, though," answered Mr. Price. "It's really the beginning of holiday time."

"Won't it be smashing!" interrupted Joanna. "We'll be off first thing in the morning."

"Not first thing," retorted Mr. Price. "It's a pity we have to travel on a Bank Holiday, but there it is —we can't do anything about it. There'll be streams of cars on the road. But if we go in the middle of the

morning, we should miss the worst traffic."

"Why is it called a Bank Holiday?" asked Stephen.

"Well, throughout the year the banks are open every day except Saturdays and Sundays. But there are special days when the banks close, in England these are Christmas Day, Boxing Day, New Year's Day, Good Friday, Easter Monday, Spring Holiday and the late Summer Holiday which is usually a Monday at the end of August—and these are called Bank Holidays. On these days nearly everyone else has a holiday too. Good idea, isn't it?"

"You bet," said Stephen. "The best thing about school is the holidays!"

"You rascal," commented Mrs. Price. "You don't mean that. In spite of all the fuss you make about school, you enjoy it most of the time!"

"Ahem! Change the subject!" suggested Mr. Price. "What did Mr. Hill preach about this morning?"

"The Holy Spirit."

"Yes, but what did he say about the Holy Spirit?"

Joanna answered first. "He said the Holy Spirit is the gift of God the Father and the Lord Jesus to Christians."

"That's right," replied Mr. Price. "Anything else, Steve?"

"God the Father and the Lord Jesus sent Him because They had promised to."

Joanna nodded in agreement. "He was sent to stay with Christians for ever. He will never leave them. Right up to the time Christians die, He stays with them."

"Yes," added Stephen, "and He was sent to live in us. We can't see Him living in us, but He does if we trust in the Lord Jesus."

Mrs. Price was pleased to see how much the twins remembered. "Just as this house is your home," she explained, "the Holy Spirit wants to make our lives His home."

"What's worrying you, Jo?" enquired Mr. Price, seeing that Joanna looked puzzled.

"Well, sometimes you and Mummy talk about the Lord Jesus living in us when we trust Him. And then sometimes you talk about the Holy Spirit living in us. Our Sunday School teachers do the same. Do they both live in us? Or just one?"

"Let me ask you a question first," replied Mr. Price. "There's God the Father. There's God the Son. And there's God the Holy Spirit. Does that mean three Gods?"

"Of course not, Daddy!" replied Joanna. "You've explained that before."

"Good," answered Mr. Price. "There's only one God. If we're Christians, we can say that God the Father lives in us. Or we can say, Jesus lives in us. Or we can say the Holy Spirit lives in us. In fact, each of these things is true. But we know that God the Father and the Lord Jesus are in heaven, and that it is the Holy Spirit who is here on earth. It is the Holy Spirit, therefore, who lives in the

Christian. But the Holy Spirit and the Lord Jesus are so much one that it is really the Father and the Lord Jesus living in us too."

"But when we trust in the Lord Jesus and the Holy Spirit lives in us, what is He there for?" asked Stephen. "What does He do in us?"

"That's like asking what is the use of the air that we breathe, Steve!" exclaimed Mr. Price. "You can't live without air, and we can't live as God wants us to live without the Holy Spirit's help."

"But *how* does He help us?"

"First of all, He helps us to understand what it means to be a Christian. Most of us are very muddled about this to start with. Sometimes people think that being a Christian is going to church. Or perhaps they think it's only a matter of trying to do their best and helping people when they can. But the Holy Spirit speaks to us through the Bible, when we hear it taught and preached, and shows us that being a Christian is turning from our sin and then trusting and obeying the Lord Jesus. Suddenly, perhaps, you feel that God is speaking just to you and no one else."

"I know," said Stephen. "At the Sunday School Anniversary I felt just like that. When the speaker told us about the two kingdoms—Satan's and God's —I knew what he meant. I saw I could become a member of God's kingdom only by trusting in the Lord Jesus; I'd known it for a long time, but I felt that God was really speaking to me. I forgot everyone else. I knew that I must ask God to forgive my sins. And I asked the Lord Jesus to be my Saviour and Master—just as the speaker said we should."

Mr. Price nodded; he understood what had happened. "That was the work of the Holy Spirit. He was helping you to understand what the Bible teaches us about being a Christian. And He'll keep on teaching us. Most of all, He wants us to be like the Lord Jesus. Sometimes He'll make our conscience worry us when we've done something wrong or haven't done something we should have done. Do you remember when we passed that tramp last holiday?"

"I remember," said Joanna. "We noticed him as we walked through the shops down to the sea. We pointed at him, and you told us not to be rude. Then after we'd gone past, you went back and bought him a hot-dog."

"You've got a good memory," said Mr. Price with a smile. "When I first saw the tramp I thought, 'He looks hungry'. Then I thought, 'But he must be lazy; he doesn't deserve to be helped'. But as we walked on, my conscience made me feel uncomfortable. I thought, 'Jesus would have helped him'. I knew then that I must go back and give him something to eat. I'm sure it was the Holy Spirit helping me to see what I should do. It's so easy to be selfish, but the Holy Spirit won't let us stay that way, if we're prepared to listen to Him."

Mr. Price looked across the table at Mrs. Price.

"Is there anything I've forgotten?" he asked.

"You haven't said much about the way He helps us to understand the Bible and also to pray," she suggested.

"You're right; I haven't. Yes, the Holy Spirit helps us to understand the Bible as we read it. He's the best person to do this because He helped the men who wrote the books of the Bible. Every time we read the Bible, we should ask the Holy Spirit to help us to understand it; and He does. He also helps us to pray, especially if we ask Him to. And there's another thing," he added. "He makes us brave and courageous to serve God. Do you remember Peter saying he didn't know Jesus?"

"You mean in front of the servant girl, when Jesus was going to be crucified, Daddy?"

"That's right, Jo. What made the difference that first Whitsun—the Day of Pentecost, it was—when Peter spoke so bravely to thousands of people all at once about the Lord Jesus?"

"The Holy Spirit," remembered Stephen.

His father nodded. "And whenever we serve God, it's the Holy Spirit who helps us so that we're not afraid."

Mrs. Price looked at the clock. "Time we cleared away, everybody."

"Wait a minute, Mum," cried Joanna. "How do you know if the Holy Spirit is in you?"

Mr. Price smiled. "How do you know that you're alive, Jo?"

She thought for a moment. "Well, I was born; I've just eaten my dinner. And I do all sorts of things which prove I'm alive."

"You've helped to answer your own question, then," explained her father. "If you've been born into God's family by receiving the Lord Jesus into your life as your Lord and Saviour, you've received the Holy Spirit. And if you find you're hungry for the Bible—you want to read it and obey it—and your life becomes more and more like that of the Lord Jesus, then you may be sure that the Holy Spirit lives in you."

"Volunteers for drying up?" called Mrs. Price.

As he helped to stack the plates ready for clearing away, Mr. Price pointed at Stephen and Joanna with a laugh.

"You and you," he said.

3
Holidays at last

Monday morning saw the Prices up early. As usual the twins were awake before their parents, and had difficulty in keeping quiet, they were so excited. At half past six they crept downstairs and put the kettle on for tea. They knew this would be a good excuse for waking up their mother and father!

Joanna tried hard to carry the cups up on the tray without spilling any tea in the saucers; but she failed as usual.

"You're an old wobbler!" teased Stephen.

"I can't help it," said Joanna. "I try my hardest."

"Hey, what's all the noise?" called their father from the bedroom. "Get back into bed and go to sleep, you two."

"It's a quarter to seven, Daddy," shouted Stephen.

"Yes, and we've made you a cup of tea," added Joanna.

"All right, then!" Mrs. Price gave in. "Bring it in please, and in a few minutes I'll come down and get breakfast."

Joanna carefully tipped the tea from the saucers back into the cups.

"Old wobbler's carried the tea up this morning," explained Stephen airily.

"Don't tease, you rascal," said his mother, taking the tea quickly before it got spilt again.

*   *   *

As soon as breakfast was over, Stephen and Joanna started bringing down all the things they wanted to take away on holiday.

"What time are we leaving, Mummy?" asked Joanna. "I do want to get there."

"When we're ready!" answered her mother, who was busy in the kitchen. "We can't leave everything untidy for Grannie and Grandad."

At that moment Stephen came out of his bedroom and ran straight into his father who was carrying a suitcase downstairs.

"Mind where you're going, Steve!"

"Sorry, Dad. I was just fetching another game in case it rains, and we have to stay indoors."

Mr. Price looked at the pile of games and books that Stephen had made in the hall and groaned. "We can't take all that! I'll need a lorry, not a small car, to take everything at this rate. We're not moving house, you know—just going away for a week!"

Mrs. Price guessed what the twins were up to. "Two books each, and two games each, that's all," she said firmly. "And no more getting in the way, running up and down stairs. Go and sit in the front room and read until everything's in the car. I shan't be long now."

Reluctantly Stephen and Joanna did as they were told. Stephen had his father's guide-book in his blazer pocket, so the time passed quickly.

* * *

"We're still looking for car numbers, Daddy," Joanna explained.

"What number are you up to?"

"Nineteen," replied Joanna. "We've been looking for a car or a van or a bike with a number twenty for ages and ages. I hope we see one today."

But by the time they were halfway there, the twins still hadn't seen a twenty. They decided they would play another game if they didn't see one soon. As they had been travelling for about an hour and a half, Mr. Price suggested stopping at the next lay-by for a snack.

The lay-by was at the top of a hill and there was a beautiful view; Stephen and Joanna really felt they were on holiday now.

"What were you looking at when we were packing the car?" asked Mrs. Price. "It certainly kept you quiet!"

"Daddy's guide-book," replied Joanna.

"Yes; and Daddy, there's a Saxon-Norman church in a village a mile and a half from where we'll be staying. The village is at the bottom of the downs. Can we go there?"

"If you can tell me who the Saxons were,"

answered his father with a smile.

"That's easy," replied Stephen. "They were people who came from north Germany in the fifth and sixth centuries."

"How did you know that, Steve?" His mother was surprised at his knowing the answer so well. "Have you been told it at school?"

"No," he said, "it was in our magazine. There were lots of pictures of churches as old as this one."

"Doesn't it go back a long time!" exclaimed Joanna. "When was the very first church, Daddy?"

"Do you mean the first church in England?"

"No, the first anywhere."

"That's rather difficult to answer," her father explained. "The first Christians were Jews living in or visiting Jerusalem. They used to meet in the temple if they lived in Jerusalem, or in a synagogue anywhere else. 'Synagogue' is the name of the building where Jews meet to worship God. Later on they couldn't do this because they were forced to leave the temple and the synagogues."

"Why, Dad?"

"Because many of the Jews refused to believe that Jesus is the Messiah—the person they had been looking for ever since the Old Testament first promised He would come."

"Charles, my friend at school, is Jewish," interrupted Stephen. "Is that why he goes out when we have Scripture and only comes into assembly for the notices, after we've had prayers?"

"Yes."

"What happened to the Christians then?" enquired Joanna.

"Well, they met in one another's homes. Some
of the early Christians had large homes; many of
them didn't, of course, because they were slaves
who lived in their masters' houses."

"Did the slaves and masters meet together if they
were Christians?" asked Stephen.

"Yes, that's one of the wonderful things about the
Christian Church. When people trust in the Lord
Jesus, they know that they should love one another
as brothers and sisters, whether they are rich or
poor."

"It doesn't matter about the colour of their skin
either, does it?" Stephen remembered the many
coloured boys and girls who went to his school.
"We've got lots of West Indian boys in our class."

"That's right, Steve," nodded Mr. Price. "I'm
afraid sometimes people are unkind to coloured
people. But Christians should never be unkind. The
Lord Jesus loves us all the same, whether we have
red, yellow, black or white skin; and He wants us
to love everyone."

Joanna liked the thought of masters and slaves all
meeting together in a home to worship God. "They
must have been squashed sometimes," she remarked.

"Yes, that's why later on the Christians had to
put up special buildings. But remember, a building

isn't really the Church."

Stephen looked puzzled. "What do you mean, Dad?"

"A Church isn't a building put up in a special way, but a group of people who love the Lord Jesus, meeting together to worship and serve Him."

"When did the Church begin, then, Daddy?" asked Joanna.

"The first Whitsun was the birthday of the Church, Jo. When the Holy Spirit came down on the apostles, they preached the good news about Jesus. Lots of people believed in the Lord Jesus, and became Christians. And they were the beginning of the Church."

"Time we moved on, Daddy," interrupted Mrs. Price.

"Let's keep on looking for car numbers," suggested Stephen, "but let's do something else as well."

"Such as?" asked Joanna.

"See who can spot a haystack first."

"That's easy—got one!"

"Where?"

"Your hair!" said Joanna with a grin.

4
The old church

The Prices arrived at the bungalow just before tea-time. Grannie and Grandad had left it all tidy. There was a note from Grannie on the mantelpiece, which Stephen spotted at once.

"Look, Mummy," he cried. "Grannie's left a note. She says that she's put a surprise for Joanna and me in our bedrooms—can we go and see what she's left you."

"Good old Grannie! She never forgets you, does she? All right, go and see what she's left you."

Joanna and Stephen rushed off to their bedrooms. They each found on their bed a brown-paper parcel. Joanna managed to get hers open first. Inside she found a box of different games: there were snakes and ladders, ludo, tiddly-winks and draughts. By the time she'd read out what was on the box, Stephen had opened his parcel. It had two lovely new jigsaw puzzles inside; one had 500 pieces and the other had 750 pieces.

"Aren't they good?" Joanna said.

"Mmmm," said Stephen. "Look, there's a note tucked in the side of the box."

"And in mine," exclaimed Joanna. "It says, 'Please share these with each other.'"

Mr. Price had been carrying the cases in and had heard the twins talking about their surprises.

"Grannie knows you two very well!" he said laughingly. "Just you do what she says, and share them properly."

"We won't squabble, Daddy," replied Joanna. "Hey, can I do one of your puzzles, please, Steve?"

"Not till I've done them both first," said Stephen indignantly.

"Beast," said Joanna.

"I thought you weren't going to squabble, Steve!" interrupted Mr. Price. "I suggest you put them all away until after tea anyway. Then perhaps we can all play a game together."

*　　*　　*

Next day the weather was beautiful. The sky was clear, and it seemed it was going to be hot. The twins went out with their father after breakfast to the row of shops near the bungalow. It didn't take long to explore them. They found a newsagent where Mr. Price bought his newspaper; the window of a well-stocked toy shop attracted the twins, and they promised themselves a visit later on.

"Where would you like to go today?" asked Mr. Price. "We could go down to the beach, if you like. The weather's good, though I'm afraid there's quite a wind. But it'll probably get hotter later on. Or we could go out for a ride in the country."

"Can we go to that Saxon-Norman church, please, Daddy?" asked Joanna. "You know, the one we told you about in the car."

"Ooh, yes please," said Stephen.

Mr. Price smiled. "The old church it is then," he replied. "How do we get there?"

Stephen and Joanna had the answer all prepared. They had studied the guide-book carefully, and had written down the numbers of the roads they needed to follow.

*   *   *

"We're off on a mystery tour," Mr. Price explained to his wife as they all set off in the car.

"I can guess where," replied Mrs. Price. "We're going to find that church, I expect. I knew the twins wouldn't forget your promise, not after Steve was able to tell you so well who the Saxons were."

Stephen hadn't told Joanna to keep a look-out for car numbers, as he wanted to see a number twenty before her. But Joanna hadn't forgotten, and suddenly she cried, "There's one!"

"What?" asked her mother.

"A number twenty," answered Joanna, "on that tractor we've just passed."

"Wish I'd seen it first," grumbled Stephen. "O.K., twenty-one now."

"Let's forget car numbers for a moment and look for the signpost to the village where the church is," Mr. Price knew they were getting near. "Look, is that it?"

A few minutes later, they were in the village, and found the church right in the centre. They parked the car near the side entrance and walked up the steps into the churchyard.

"Look at that old tower," shouted Stephen. "I bet that's the Saxon part, and the rest is Norman."

"You're probably right," agreed his father. "There are more Saxon towers left than complete churches."

"How can you tell the difference between the Saxon and the Norman parts?" Mrs. Price asked. "It's long time since I was at school!"

"You tell me if I'm wrong, twins," said Mr. Price, as he began to explain. "The Saxon churches had narrow windows and rounded arches and door-ways. The Norman churches were often bigger, with large round arches, and round pillars to support them. Their towers looked more like the towers of a castle. The Normans often carved animals and men in the stone, too."

The churchyard was beautifully kept; people must have spent a long time planting the flowers and taking care of them.

"Here's the hymnbook they use, Daddy," Joanna said, picking one up from a pew. "It isn't the same as we use."

"There are lots of different hymnbooks," her father explained. "Where's Stephen got to?"

"I'm up here, Daddy," called Stephen. "I've always wondered what it was like to be in a pulpit! Isn't it beautifully carved? It must have taken ages."

"I think you should come down from there, Steve," said Mrs. Price anxiously. "And don't leave any fingermarks—everything's so wonderfully polished."

"Yes, Mum," interrupted Joanna, "you can smell the polish—just like when you go back to school at the beginning of term."

Mr. Price nodded in agreement. "The people who belong to this church," he said, "must love it very much and work hard to keep it so well."

"I wonder how many there are?" Stephen said. "And how do you belong to a church, Daddy?"

"What do you mean?" asked Mr. Price. "Do you mean a church like this, or do you mean belonging to the Church of the Lord Jesus in every part of the world?"

"Both, I think," said Stephen.

"Well, there are different ways of belonging to the many churches you find everywhere. To belong to a church like this one, you would have to be baptised and confirmed. At baptism a child would have the sign of the cross made on his forehead with water as a kind of promise that when he was older he wouldn't be 'ashamed to confess the faith of Christ crucified and manfully to fight under His banner against sin, the world and the devil'. But, of course, this would usually take place when a child was very young, and he wouldn't know what was happening. And so at confirmation, a person makes these promises again for himself, and promises to be Christ's faithful soldier all his life."

"Was Uncle John's and Auntie Joan's baby being baptised when we went to church with them last year?" asked Joanna.

"Yes," nodded Mr. Price. "In some other churches you become a member by being baptised when you're older—at about the time you might be confirmed in a church like this. In other churches you become a member by asking to join the church, and the minister welcomes you, perhaps by shaking your hand, at a communion service."

"And what did you mean, Daddy, when you talked about belonging to the Church of the Lord Jesus in every part of the world?" asked Stephen.

"I'll try to explain," Mr. Price said. "Every group of Christians meeting in a church or building is only a small part of God's true Church which is to be found throughout the world. You could be called a member of a church like this, or any other church, without really being a member of God's true Church. It's very important to belong to God's Church, which is made up of His children everywhere."

"How do you belong to that Church, then?" Joanna persisted.

"By a living faith in the Lord Jesus, Jo," answered Mr. Price. "Look, there's a lion on the top of that pillar! No, only a stone one! But outside in the field next to the church there's a horse. What's the difference between them? Well, one has no life, and the other has. Our faith in the Lord Jesus must be a real and living faith if we're to belong to the Church of the Lord Jesus."

"What do you mean, Dad? I don't really understand," said Stephen.

"Think of two boys," said his father. "One's called Bill and the other's called John. You tell me which has a living faith if I tell you what they can say truthfully about the Lord Jesus. Bill says, 'I believe that Jesus lived here on earth and died on the cross.' John says, 'I believe that Jesus lived here on earth and died for me on the cross. I have asked Him to be my Saviour.' Which boy has the living faith, do you think?"

"John," answered Stephen.

"That's right," agreed Mr. Price. "Think of it another way. Here's my bunch of keys: only one of them fits the front door of Grannie and Grandad's bungalow. Now the only key which will open the door of God's Church is faith in the Lord Jesus. The key of 'trying your best' or 'being a church member' won't open the door. Only the key of trusting in the Lord Jesus will do."

"I think I understand," said Stephen. "When you ask the Lord Jesus Christ to become your Saviour, and you believe in Him, you then belong to His Church, with its members all over the world."

"Yes, that's right."

"Well," asked Stephen, "if you belong to the Church of Jesus everywhere, why do you have to belong to a church like this one as well?"

Mr. and Mrs. Price laughed. "That's a good question, Steve," said Mrs. Price. "I think you'd better let Daddy answer that later on. Your cousin Mark joined his church last week: perhaps Daddy will explain to you why."

"Can we buy a postcard of the church in the shop in the village, if it sells them?" asked Joanna.

"Perhaps the shop will sell ice-cream too," added Stephen innocently.

"Perhaps . . ." said Mr. Price, with a laugh.

5
Questions at bedtime

As far as Stephen and Joanna were concerned, the holiday had got off to a good start; they had especially enjoyed the visit to the Saxon-Norman church. Joanna had bought a postcard—not to send it to anyone, but because she wanted to take it home to show her school friends where she had been. And they *had* sold ice cream in the shop.

They spent the afternoon on the beach. The sun stayed out all the time, and the water was quite warm. The hours just seemed to fly, and the afternoon passed in no time.

They arrived back at the bungalow rather hot and sticky.

"Do you know," exclaimed Mrs. Price in surprise, "it's nearly six o'clock. I'd no idea it was so late. I thought we'd have a big tea today, as we only had sandwiches at dinner time."

"How long will it take you to cook?" asked Mr. Price.

"I'll need about an hour."

"Let me make a suggestion, twins: you two must have a bath this evening, to get rid of all that sand;

you oughtn't to have a bath after a large tea, so I suggest you both have one quickly now, then you'll be ready for bed before tea."

"Have tea in our pyjamas!" cried Stephen.

"Yes; it won't matter for once. The Queen's not likely to visit us!"

"Can we play some games afterwards, then?" asked Joanna.

"All right. I'll have a game of ludo with the first person to have a bath and get dressed!"

Stephen and Joanna raced to the bathroom as fast as they could.

"I've never seen you two so eager for a bath!" commented Mrs. Price. "Ladies first, Steve. While Jo has her bath, you play a game with Daddy. That'll be fair."

*   *   *

Joanna and Stephen were very good at making excuses for staying up late. At eight o'clock they were still playing draughts, and had made their father promise to play the winner.

"Cousin Mark's good at draughts, isn't he, Steve?"

"Yes; but he's much older than us, so he ought to be!"

"Did you say that he became a member of his church last Sunday, Dad?"

"That's right, Jo. I want to write and tell him how pleased we are about it."

"Will you answer my question now, please, Dad? The one about why you have to belong to a church?"

His father smiled. Trust Steve to think he could stay up later by asking questions!

Mrs. Price knew what her husband was thinking. "I did suggest you'd tell him," she said. "They can stay up a little longer as we're on holiday."

"Well," began Mr. Price, "Mark is a Christian. He put his trust in the Lord Jesus when he was away at camp last summer. There have been lots of little things which have shown that he really means to serve the Lord Jesus. One of them is that he wants to belong to the church he goes to."

"Yes, but why?" asked Stephen. "You can still go to a church without belonging to it, can't you?"

"First of all, Mark has joined his church because he knows that a Christian can't live the Christian life on his own. The Bible uses pictures—not drawings, but word pictures—to tell us what the Church is like. All these pictures remind us that Christians need one another."

"What sort of pictures, Dad?" asked Joanna.

"It describes the Church as a flock, a building, a body and a family—to mention just some."

"Can you have a building made of one brick?" Mrs. Price joined in.

"No."

"Can you have a flock with just one sheep?"

"Of course not."

"Is an ear any use without the rest of the body?"

"No!"

"Can you have a family with just one person?"

"No!"

"Good," Mrs. Price went on, "when the Bible describes the Church as a flock, a building, a body and a family, it's telling us that the Christian isn't meant to live the Christian life on his own. He's to live it with the help of other Christians."

"I think I understand that," nodded Stephen. "But why does God want Christians to join a church?"

"That's easy," replied Mr. Price. "There are things God wants Christians to do together. He's pleased when Christians meet to praise Him by singing; of course, Christians can sing hymns on their own, but God is specially pleased when they sing together. The same is true of prayer. God hears us when we pray to Him on our own, but He's glad when Christians pray together. And then there are certain things God has told us to do—like baptism and the Communion service."

"Tell us more about baptism, Daddy," requested Joanna. "And what happens at a Communion service?"

"That'll have to wait for another evening—or perhaps two evenings!" exclaimed Mr. Price. "But Christians join together for these things. And of course they serve God together: maybe by teaching children in the Sunday School, or by visiting people around the church and trying to tell them about the Lord Jesus. All these things Christians do through belonging to a local church. God wants the Christians to find work to do with other Christians. Could you play cricket just by yourself, Steve?"

"Of course not."

"Does everyone play the same part?"

"No; you can be wicketkeeper, or a fieldsman, or a bowler or a batsman."

"But is everyone important?"

"Oh, yes," said Stephen.

"The same is true in a church. You have many people and each one has some job to do which pleases God and which will help others. One man may be able to preach, and so he preaches to help others understand God's Word."

"Like Mr. Hill, at our church," remarked Stephen.

"Yes," nodded Mr. Price. "Some people are able to teach God's Word, and so they teach it in the Sunday School; others are good at doing things with their hands, so they help look after the buildings."

"You sometimes help decorate, don't you Dad?"

"Yes, Steve. It's great fun doing those kind of things together, and to know that there's something special you can do."

"Are there other jobs people can do?" asked Joanna.

"Oh, lots and lots. I can't think of them all. There are people who spend a lot of their time visiting the ill and the elderly. I'm sure that their work pleases God very much."

"What's the most important thing that goes on in a church, Daddy?"

"There's no doubt about that, Steve. It's preaching God's Word. You see, it's through God's Word that God speaks to us. God feeds our souls by His Word. What do you think is the most important thing Mummy does for us every day?"

"I know Dad," said Joanna at once. "It's cooking our meals and making sure we eat enough."

"Good. Well, God puts Christians into churches, wherever they live, so that they can be fed from God's Word. And whenever God sees Christians meeting together to hear His Word, He is pleased."

"I wonder if Mark knows all this," Joanna said quietly.

Mrs. Price smiled. "I'm sure he does. But you can ask him when he comes to see us. Time for bed now, you two!"

"Oh, no!"

"Oh, yes!"

"Can't we have just one more game of draughts, please, Mum?"

Their mother remembered about being on holiday. "One game, then," she said, pretending to be severe: "But only one!"

6

The castle and the new game

One of the most exciting days of Stephen and Joanne's holiday was the one when they went to see the ruins of an old castle. They'd been looking at the guide-book, the one that had told them about the old Saxon-Norman church, and discovered that, not many miles away from it, was a castle which went back to the time of William the Conqueror. They were very excited about this discovery because they'd had lessons at school about William the Conqueror, and there had been a series about him in their magazine.

They arrived at the village early in the afternoon, and soon came across a signpost which had written on it the words 'To the Castle'. Mr. Price drove the car up part of the way, but there wasn't a proper car park, and it was very bumpy. As soon as they stopped, Stephen and Joanna ran on ahead of their parents to see what they could find. Exploring new places was one of the best parts of a holiday.

They had to climb up steps cut into the ground. At the top, part of one of the towers of the castle was still standing.

"It doesn't look very safe, does it Steve?"

Stephen craned his neck and peered up at the uneven stonework. "No, it looks as if it's going to fall down any minute."

They explored the rest of the castle ruins; there wasn't very much left to see. Grass had grown over most of the stones, but the walls of the castle remained, and in places they were safe enough and wide enough to walk on. In a few places, though, it was quite dangerous, and Joanna wasn't sure she liked it. They looked down the steep slopes to where the moat had been.

"It's great here, Jo. When I get back to school, I'm going to tell Mrs. Foxleigh all about it," said Stephen. "And I'm going to make a drawing of it; I think I can remember where all the towers are."

"Me too. And we can look in the guide-book and find out when it was built."

By the time they were back in the car, it was almost time to think about making their way home. But the weather was so splendid that Mr. Price said that they could go home a long way round to make the most of the fine afternoon.

"What game shall we play?" asked Stephen. "Could we look out for things?"

"All right," agreed Mr. Price.

Near where the Prices were staying, there were estate agents called 'Fox and Smith'. Their signs, 'For Sale', 'To Let' or 'Sold' could be seen outside many houses and flats. One of the games the twins had played before was seeing who could spot one of these notice boards first. The first one to see the sign board would shout out 'Fox and Smith'! (Which must have sounded very odd to anyone else who happened to hear.) But now they were too far away to see any of that estate agent's signs, so they had to think of something else.

"Why don't we look for churches this time," suggested Mrs. Price. "Let's see how many we can spot before we get home. We'll be passing through lots of villages and two towns. You'll see several different kinds of church."

"Good idea," said Joanna. "We've never done that before."

So as they went along, Stephen and Joanna tried to look through all the windows of the car at once to see who could spot the churches first.

"Look! There's one," shouted Stephen. They couldn't see yet what the name of the church was, but it wasn't long before they drove right past it.

"It's St. Paul's Church, Daddy," cried Stephen. "It's Church of England, like the church we go to near the bungalow."

"Oh, look!" exclaimed Joanna. "There's another church on the other side of the road." It was a Roman Catholic church.

Joanne had a pencil and paper and she wrote down the names of all the churches they saw, although the speed of the car made it hard to write clearly.

"There's another one," she shouted suddenly. 'It says United Reformed Church.''

They drove through one of the towns and saw several Church of England churches; one of them was called 'St. Michael and All Angels'. "That's a long name for a church, isn't it, Dad?" Stephen commented.

They were surprised at the large number of churches they discovered. They saw a Baptist Church, a Methodist Church and a Salvation Army Hall, all quite near to each other.

By the time they were nearly home, the twins had made quite a long list. They had seen twenty

Church of England churches, four Roman Catholic, two Baptist, three Methodist, two United Reformed churches, two Salvation Army halls, another hall (which Mr. Price explained was the place where the Christian Brethren met), a Pentecostal and an Evangelical Free Church.

"How many churches have we seen altogether?" asked Stephen. "Let's count up. One, two, three . . ." There was a long pause. "Thirty-six!"

"Phew!" exclaimed Joanna. "What a lot of churches! And you know, Dad," she added, "some of them were almost next door to one another. In one of the villages, there was a Methodist church right next to the Church of England. I should think you'd get mixed up and go into the wrong church!"

"Daddy," said Stephen, "why aren't all the churches called the same? Why are some called 'Church of England' and others 'Baptist' churches and 'United Reformed' churches?"

Mr. Price smiled. "That's a hard question. Really all the churches are called the same."

"What do you mean, Daddy?" said Joanna.

"Well, they're all called *churches*, and they would all think of themselves as *Christian* churches. The creed we said in the Church of England service begins 'I believe in God the Father . . .'—do you remember the creed?"

Stephen and Joanna nodded.

"Well, *all* the Christians in *all* these churches

would believe the creed, and would be glad to say so. If you said to the people in these different churches, 'What makes a church?' most of them would say, 'A church is a group of people who love the Lord Jesus and want to serve and obey Him'. The names of the churches are the results of events in the history of our country."

"What do the names mean, Daddy?" asked Joanna.

"Most of the names don't show what the churches believe about the important facts of the Christian faith, because all these churches believe that Jesus is the Son of God, that He came into the world to save us from our sins, and that if we trust Him as our Saviour our sins are forgiven, and we receive the gift of everlasting life. Most of their different names show how they're governed, or some special teaching they feel to be very important."

"What do you mean by 'how they're governed'?" asked Stephen.

"Well, every church has to be governed, or kept in order, rather like schools. You have to have a headmistress or a headmaster in a school, and perhaps a deputy headmaster or mistress as well."

"Oh, yes," interrupted Joanna. "There's a deputy headmistress at our school, Mrs. Biggs—she takes the second years."

"And then," continued Mr. Price, "you often have prefects or monitors."

"Monitors," said Stephen.

"What would your school do without a head-master or mistress, or monitors?"

"I don't know," laughed Joanna. "Things would get into a lovely muddle; they do now sometimes!"

"It's the same in the church," explained Mr. Price. "You need to have people to govern the church, but often they have different names in different churches, and do things in different ways, just as in some schools you have prefects, and in others you have monitors."

"How is the Church of England we go to here on holiday different from our church at home, then, Daddy?" asked Stephen.

"Well," said his father, "in the Church of England the people who govern the church are the bishops. But in our church at home it's the elders and deacons who do this—they look after only one church, but a bishop looks after lots of churches."

"What happens at the United Reformed church?" enquired Stephen.

"They are governed by elders, too, who guide their own local church and sometimes help to govern a group of churches. Usually the people who belong to the church appoint their own leaders."

"What about the Baptist church?" Stephen was looking down his list.

"A Baptist church is really like the United Reformed church in the way it's governed. But it's called a 'Baptist' church because its members believe that only grown-ups should be baptised, and not little children or babies like our holiday church."

"You still haven't told us about baptism, Daddy."

"There's not time now, Jo. Mark's coming to-morrow; why don't you ask him about it? But there's one thing I do want you to remember and understand."

"What's that?" enquired Stephen.

"Although churches have different names, true Christians know that the most important thing about a church isn't its name, but the fact that the good news of the Lord Jesus is taught and preached from the Bible. I don't mind what the name of a church is, as long as it's truly loyal to the Lord Jesus—that's what matters most."

"We could spot churches again tomorrow," said Joanna at bed-time.

"How many did we see today?"

"Thirty-six."

"I don't expect we'll ever find any more than that on one day," said Stephen sleepily.

Mrs. Price laughed. "I don't know," she said. "Instead of counting sheep when you can't get to sleep, you'll be counting churches!"

"I'll try it!" said Joanna eagerly.

But there was no need.

7
Cousin Mark

Joanna and Stephen were very excited when they awoke up on Saturday morning: Mark was coming to visit them! He had sent a post-card the day before to say he would be on the 10.31 train. The twins had made all kinds of plans for what they wanted to show him while he stayed with them for the week-end. Mr. and Mrs. Price reminded them that Mark was coming to enjoy some of their holiday, and was not to be rushed off his feet here, there and everywhere. But they knew that Mark enjoyed being with the twins, and was well able to keep them under control.

The twins were determined not to be late at the station, and worried their father so much that at a quarter past ten they were waiting on the platform. It seemed ages before the train arrived. At last lots of people started to pour through the ticket-barrier; but Mark was nowhere to be seen. Then suddenly Joanna spotted him.

"There he is!"

"We thought you weren't coming, Mark," explained Mr. Price.

"I'm afraid I nearly missed the train! I had to get

into the very last compartment, so I had to walk further than everyone else! It's good to see you all."

"We've got lots of things to do," said Stephen excitedly.

"We're going to take you to the downs straight away," added Joanna.

"Hey, wait a moment!" Mr. Price interrupted. "We're going home first to give Mark a cup of coffee; *then* perhaps we'll go for a ride before lunch!"

*   *   *

Three-quarters of an hour later, Mark and the twins were in the car again with Mr. Price, on their way to the top of the downs—a favourite place. They went for a short walk through the corn fields, looking for wild flowers, while Mr. Price stayed with the car. There was a magnificent view from the top of the downs, and they sat down for a moment to rest before making their way back to the car.

"Have you had a good holiday, Mark? What have you been doing?"

"I went to camp with some of the boys from my church," answered Mark. "There were twenty of us altogether! Would you like to see some of the photos I took?"

"Ooh, yes!"

Mark produced a folder from his pocket, and Stephen and Joanna examined the photos with interest.

"I shouldn't think the boys liked doing the wash-

ing-up, did they, Mark?" enquired Joanna.

"Oh, it was fun really. I don't expect things were as clean as at home though!"

"Did all the boys come from your church?" asked Stephen.

"Yes."

"Daddy was telling us that you've become a member of your church."

"That's right. Just before I went to camp."

"We were talking to Daddy about belonging to a church, and about baptism," Joanna went on to explain. "Daddy said we ought to ask you some of our questions."

"What do you want to know?"

"We were wondering why Christians are baptised,' said Joanna.

"I think the answer to that is simple," Mark said thoughtfully. "Jesus said He wanted all His disciples to be baptised, and He set an example by being baptised Himself. Do you remember? John the Baptist baptised lots of Jewish people in the river Jordan. One day Jesus came from Galilee to be baptised, but John tried to stop Jesus, because he knew that Jesus hadn't sinned, and that baptism was a sign that people were sorry for their sins and wanted to please God. So John said to Jesus, 'I shouldn't baptise you. I need you to baptise me.' But Jesus replied, 'It is right for us to meet all the Law's demands, to do everything God wants us to do. So I want you to go ahead and baptise me now.' Jesus didn't need to be baptised like the other people because He'd never sinned, but He wanted to set an example in everything, so that we should know what He wanted us to do."

"I remember having a lesson about Jesus' baptism in Sunday School," added Stephen. "When Jesus came out of the water, the heavens opened—or something; and Jesus saw the Spirit of God coming down like a dove and resting on Him."

"Yes," continued Joanna, "and they all heard a voice, which said, 'This is my dearly loved Son, in whom I am well pleased'."

"That's right," agreed Mark. "I'm quite sure that Jesus wants us to be baptised because when He was saying 'Goodbye' to the disciples, after His resurrection, He told them to go and make disciples of all the nations and baptise them in the name of the Father, the Son and the Holy Spirit. So wherever the apostles and the disciples went, they told people that if they wanted to follow Jesus, they must be baptised."

"But why is baptism so important, Mark?" asked Stephen. "You can follow the Lord Jesus without being baptised, can't you?"

"I suppose you could," replied Mark. "But baptism is a bit like a badge; it shows that we really mean to follow Jesus. I expect you wear a badge on your blazer when you're at home."

"Oh, yes! I wear a Scripture Union badge, so does Steve."

"Do you wear a badge on the pocket, too, to show which school you go to?"

"Yes, we do," answered Stephen. "I hadn't thought of that one."

"Well," continued Mark, "could you belong to your school or to Scripture Union without wearing a badge?"

"Of course we could."

"Why do you have a badge, then?"

"I suppose," said Stephen, "to show that we do belong to that school, and to Scripture Union, and that we're glad we belong to them."

"That's just why baptism's so important," explained Mark. "A person could trust in the Lord Jesus and want to follow Him without being baptised, but it would be rather strange. If you really trust in Jesus and serve Him, you want people to know, and you're not ashamed about it. Baptism's like wearing a badge. When you read the New Testament, you soon find that everyone who trusted in the Lord Jesus was baptised. Do you remember the story of the Ethiopian?"

"I think so," said Stephen doubtfully.

"Wasn't Philip something to do with it?"

"Yes, Jo. God told Philip to go down from Jerusalem to Gaza. It was a desert road, and a lonely journey. But Philip knew that he must obey God. As he made his way through the desert, an Ethiopian came by in a chariot. He was an important member of the Ethiopian government—the treasurer to the Queen. He was on his way home after visiting Jerusalem to worship, and he was sitting in his chariot, reading part of the Old Testament. God's Spirit told Philip to go over to the chariot. As Philip ran forward, he heard the man reading the prophet Isaiah, and he asked, 'Do you understand what you're reading?' And the Ethiopian said, 'How can I, unless someone helps me, and explains it to me?' And he invited Philip to sit by his side. Now the passage the Ethiopian was reading was all about how the Lord Jesus died on the cross for our sins. When he had read the passage through to Philip, the Ethiopian said, 'Tell me, please, who is the prophet talking about? Himself or someone else?' Then Philip began at the part of the Bible which the Ethiopian had been reading, and told him the good news about Jesus. He must have told him, too, that if he was going to show others that he trusted in the Lord Jesus as his Saviour and had become one of His disciples, he would have to be baptised: because as they went along the road, they came to some water, and the Ethiopian said, 'Look, here's some water. Is there any reason why I shouldn't be baptised now?' Philip told him that if he really believed in the Lord Jesus, there was no reason at all why he shouldn't. So the Ethiopian gave orders for the chariot to stop, and both of them went down into the water, and Philip baptised him. The Ethiopian went home, knowing now that he didn't belong to himself any more, but to the Lord Jesus."

"Is that what baptism means as well?" asked Stephen. "That you don't belong to yourself any more?"

"Yes," nodded Mark. "When a person's baptised, he's baptised in the name of the Lord Jesus. If a man sells a house, instead of the house being in his name —belonging to him—it passes into the name of someone else, the man it's going to belong to. When we're baptised in the name of the Lord Jesus, we know that because He died for us, we have no right to say that we belong to ourselves. We now belong to the Lord Jesus, and we're baptised into His name so that He can do just what He wants with our life, because we want to live for Him."

Mark paused. "Have I answered all your questions?"

"I think so," said Stephen. "And it's getting late. Daddy'll be getting tired of waiting for us; and I expect it's nearly dinner time. What is the time, Mark?"

"Ten past twelve."

"We'd better run. Race you!"

They were puffed out when they reached the car.

"Thought you were never coming," said Mr. Price, starting the engine. "Your mother will be after us!"

"Sorry, Uncle," Mark apologised. "We forgot all about the time, we were too busy talking."

"Well, that's nothing new!" said Mr. Price with a grin.

8
All over

Stephen and Joanna were glad of any excuse to get up early in the morning, rather than stay quiet until it was time for their parents to wake up. With cousin Mark in the bedroom next door, they thought it would be a fine time to have a good long talk with him all on their own. So almost as soon as it was light, they crept into Mark's bedroom, went quietly on tip-toe, one each side of the bed, and said loudly in his ear, "Wake up, sleepy-head!"

Mark shot up in bed with a start.

"Oh, it's you two, you wretches!" he said, rubbing his eyes. "Honestly, it's the middle of the night!"

"No it isn't, it's nearly half past six, and time you were awake!"

"Time I was awake!" exploded Mark. "But it's Sunday; we don't have to hurry."

"But we thought we'd come and talk to you, Mark," Joanna explained.

Mark grinned and struggled to sit up in bed properly; he didn't really mind.

And so for an hour, until it was time for Stephen

and Joanna to put the kettle on for their parents' tea, they talked about all the things they'd done on their holiday. Mark knew lots about wild flowers, and told them the names of all the flowers they'd pressed in their exercise books.

*　　*　　*

Later that morning Mr. and Mrs. Price, Mark, Stephen and Joanna all walked the short distance to the church. They arrived about five minutes before the service began; the organ was playing and most people were already in their seats. The sidesman managed to find them a pew where they could all sit together.

Stephen and Joanna knelt and prayed as their parents and Mark did; then they found the right place in the prayer book, where it said 'Morning Prayer'. As the service began, the twins followed it carefully in the book. When the notices were given out, the rector of the church announced, "At the end of this service, there will be a service of Holy Communion. We invite all who know and love the Lord Jesus Christ to stay with us."

Stephen and Joanna wondered whether their parents would stay. When the last hymn had been sung, and the blessing said, Stephen whispered to Mark, "I expect Mummy and Daddy will stay; will you, Mark?"

"Yes, I will if they do," said Mark. "I'd like to."

"Mummy, may we stay and watch, please, like we did once at home?" asked Joanna.

"Is that all right, do you think, dear?" Mrs. Price turned to her husband.

Mr. Price nodded; he thought it would be good for the twins to see a Communion service in a church quite different from their own.

Stephen and Joanna were surprised when people left their seats and went in turn to kneel at the step in front of the communion table to receive the bread and the wine. They did not like to ask any questions then because the church was very quiet. It was rather different from what they remembered of the Communion service at home. There the stewards had brought round a plate with the bread and then, afterwards, they had brought round the wine, and everyone had drunk from a little cup or glass, at the same time. The twins watched and listened carefully, and by the end of the service they were simply bursting with questions.

When they were outside again, and had shaken hands with the curate at the door, Stephen said to Mark, "Why did you have to go to the front?"

"Oh, they nearly always do that in the Church of England," explained Mark. "In some churches people sit in their seats and the bread and wine are brought round to them, and in others they go to the table to receive them. But that's not really the most important thing."

"What is the most important thing, then?"

"That we remember the Lord Jesus."

"Yes; but don't we remember Him anyway?" Joanna asked. "We remembered Him in the service this morning: the preacher talked about Him."

"You're right. But Jesus told His disciples that this was a special way He wanted them—and everyone who believed in Him—to remember Him."

"When did He tell them that, Mark?" enquired Joanna.

"The night He was betrayed," Mark went on to explain. "The night Judas went out and betrayed Him, Jesus took some bread during the supper they were having together. And when He had said 'Thank you' to God for the bread, He broke it in pieces and told them to eat it, remembering that His body was given for them. Later on, when supper was more or less finished, He took the cup of wine, and told them to drink it, remembering that His blood was shed for them."

"Why did Jesus want them to remember His death like that?" Stephen asked.

"I think it was because His death on the cross was the most important event in His ministry—only by His death could we be forgiven and become His children. We've got very short memories, and He knew that. By making us remember Him in this way, we're not allowed to forget about the most important event in His life."

"Was it just ordinary bread and wine they used

in church? Would they have bought the bread in a baker's shop?" Joanna asked.

"Yes, I'm sure they did. You see, the bread and wine are just pictures."

"But why did Jesus say that we should eat the bread and drink the wine?" Stephen wanted to know. "Couldn't there be a loaf on the table to remind us of His body, and some wine to remind us of His blood, without having to eat or drink them?"

"We don't really know," Mark said slowly. "But I should think it's because eating and drinking are personal and private things. What you eat and drink becomes part of you, and gives you life and strength. If we want to become Christians, God's children, we must believe that Jesus died for us, and receive Him into our hearts, so that He becomes, as it were, part of us. And that's a very personal and private thing, just like eating bread and drinking wine."

"Can I ask you something else, Mark?"

"Yes, of course."

"What were you thinking about when you were praying as the bread and the wine were given to you?" asked Joanna shyly. "At the Communion service at home, Mummy and Daddy bowed their heads and were very quiet and still, and I wondered then what they were praying about or thinking."

"I don't know what they were thinking, of course," answered Mark. "But I expect they were doing what I was doing. When I took the bread and the wine, I thought of the cross of the Lord Jesus, and I remembered that He died for me. And I thanked Him again for dying for me, and I asked Him to help me not to forget it."

"Really, then, Mark," said Joanna, "you shouldn't take part in a Communion service unless you're a Christian?"

"No; that's why the Rector said in the notices that if you loved the Lord Jesus you were invited. Christians naturally want to come to the Lord's Table and soon, when you can really understand it all, you'll want to take communion too. The early Christians had a Communion service every Sunday, because they thought it was so important, and it helped them to remember the Lord Jesus' death."

"I'll be glad when I can go," said Stephen.

"It probably won't be long now," replied Mark. "It would be good to talk to your minister at home about it; he'll explain what it all means, and suggest the best time for you to join your church."

"That's a good idea," agreed Mr. Price. "But now, go and change into your jeans, all of you, and we'll take our lunch down to the beach. Our last visit!"

"Ugh, school tomorrow," said Stephen.

But Joanna and Mark were already out of sight.